Going
to the
Hospital

PaRragon

Bath • New York • Singapore • Hong Kong • Cologne • Delhi
Melbourne • Amsterdam • Johannesburg • Auckland • Shenzhen

Page 7

Page 9

Page 11

Page 11

Page 15

Page 16

Page 21

Page 23

Page 26

Page 29

How to use this book

 Read the story, all about Ben
and his first stay in the hospital.

 Look at each picture in the story closely.
You may be asked to find or count things
in a scene and place a sticker on the page.

 Try each activity as you go along, or read
the story first, then go back and do the
activities. The answers are at the bottom
of each activity page.

 Some pictures will need stickers to finish
the scenes or activities. Any leftover
stickers can be used to decorate your
certificate or your things.

Ben is packing his bag to go to the hospital. He is having an operation to have his tonsils removed.

Can you find 4 toy cars in the picture?

Can you find these things in the picture?

He is taking Ruffy, his teddy bear. Ben has never been to the hospital before and he is a bit scared.

Place the sticker of Ben's rocket here.

Ben is very hungry. Mom says he can't eat anything until after his operation.

"You can have a treat when it's over," she says. "I'd like ice cream, please!" says Ben.

Look at the picture on the opposite page. Can you find five differences in the picture below?

Answer

When you have finished, put the dog sticker here.

At the hospital, Ben and Mom go to the children's ward. It is very bright, with a lot of colorful pictures on the walls.

Can you find these things in the picture?

"Hello, Ben!" says a pretty lady. "I'm Nurse Natalie. I'm going to be taking care of you."

Find the sticker to finish the picture.

Place the sticker of Ben here.

Nurse Natalie takes Ben to his bed. She checks his pulse with a special machine and takes his temperature.

Mom puts Ben's pajamas, towel, and backpack in the cabinet by his bed.

Match up the pajama tops with the bottoms.

Answer

Nurse Natalie puts a name band on Ben's wrist.
She gives Ruffy one, too!

Count the cards
on Jayden's
bedside cabinet.

Can you find these things in the picture?

Ben talks to the boy in the next bed.
"I'm Jayden. I'm going home today!" he says.

Place the sticker of
the action figure here.

Jayden tells Ben that he had an operation on his tonsils, too. "My throat was a little sore, but I got some cool comic books afterward!" he says.

Find 2 stickers to finish the picture.

Which diamond does not fit in the puzzle?

a.

b.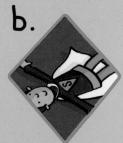

c.

d.

e.

"Time to put on your hospital gown, Ben!" says Nurse Natalie. Mom helps him to tie it up. Then it's time to go.

What does Ben have on his hospital gown?

Help Nurse Natalie to push Ben through the maze to the operating room.

How many nurses can you see altogether?

Operating room

Answer

In the operating room, Natalie puts some special cream on Ben's hand. Then the doctor gives Ben an injection to make him fall asleep.

"It doesn't hurt!" says Ben. "That's the cream," says Nurse Natalie. Ben feels very sleepy. "When you wake up, the operation will be over," she says.

Place the sticker of the doctor here.

Which of these things would you find at the hospital?

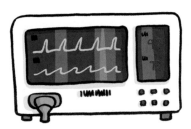

Answer

When Ben wakes up, he is in the recovery room. His throat feels a little sore. "The operation is over now," says Nurse Natalie.

Find 2 stickers to finish the picture.

Natalie wheels Ben's bed back to his room.
He still feels very sleepy. Jayden is going home.
He leaves Ben his comic books to read.

Point to the toy that is different in each row.

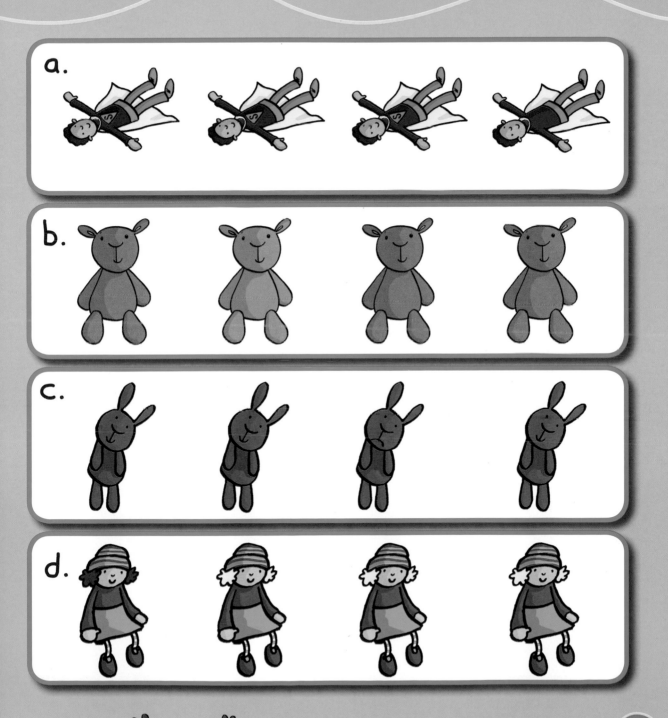

Later, Ben is eating some ice cream when his
friend Lily arrives. She has brought him a present.
"It's great! Thanks, Lily," says Ben.

Find 3 stickers
to finish the
picture.

Find the two robots that are exactly the same.

a.

b.

c.

d.

e.

f.

Ben has to stay in the hospital overnight just to make sure his throat is okay. Mom is going to sleep in a special bed next to him.

Can you find these things in the picture?

At bedtime, Mom reads Ben a comic book. "This is fun!" he says. "It's like a sleepover."

Put the sticker of Ben's dressing gown here.

The next day, Ben can go home. He leaves the comic books with Nurse Natalie. "Just in case another little boy needs them," he says, smiling.

"Thank you," says Nurse Natalie. "Would you like to choose a lollipop for being so brave?"